This Little Tiger book belongs to:

_____

_____

_____

With much love to Kerstin, Ole, baby Mia – and Loui x
~C F
This is for my little munchkins Abigail and William,
who continue to delight and inspire me
~G Y

LITTLE TIGER PRESS
1 The Coda Centre, 189 Munster Road, London SW6 6AW
www.littletigerpress.com

First published in Great Britain 2011
This edition published 2012

Text copyright © Claire Freedman 2011
Illustrations copyright © Gail Yerrill 2011
Claire Freedman and Gail Yerrill have asserted their rights
to be identified as the author and illustrator of this work under
the Copyright, Designs and Patents Act, 1988

Printed in China • LTP/1800/0391/0512

2 4 6 8 10 9 7 5 3 1

Bedtime, Little Ones!

Claire Freedman ★ _Gail Yerrill_

LITTLE TIGER PRESS
London

It's been such a happy day playing,
The setting sun glows golden red.
The little ones run home for supper,
For soon it will be time for bed.

Mummy Mouse smiles
at her children,
"Time for bed, when you've
finished your teas!"
"We're not at all tired!"
the mice chorus,
But someone's asleep
in her cheese!

It's bathtime – five rabbits are splashing,
Having fun in their big bubbly tub!
"We love to splish-splosh!" they tell Mummy,
As she gives each small bunny a scrub.

Mummy Rabbit is
drying her bunnies,
And counting them,
"One, two, three, four..."

Then she giggles,
"Wait – somebody's missing!
There should be just
one bunny more!"

The little ones snuggle round Grandpa,
As he reads to them tales from his book.
"And another!" cries one little badger.
"There's a great story here, Grandpa – look!"

Mummy Squirrel says,
"Bedtime, my babies,
Hear the sleepy-train
calling choo-choo!"
But one little squirrel's
not sleepy,
She still wants to
play peek-a-boo!

The little bears gaze at the night sky,
As silver bright stars start to peep.
"One, two, three, ZZZZ!" someone's snoring.
Star counting has sent him to sleep!

Little Rabbit is searching all over.
"Oh no!" he cries. "Where's Little Ted?
I must find my cuddly bear, Mummy,
I can't sleep without him in bed!"

All the animals have their own teddies,
To cuddle and snuggle up tight.
With each of their soft toys beside them,
They're sure to sleep soundly all night!

As Mummy Mouse
tucks up each baby,
She whispers, "Goodnight,
sleepy-head!"
Then Little Mouse
copies her Mummy,
And she tucks up her
own toy in bed.

The hedgehogs are drifting to sleep now,
As Daddy sings sweet lullabies,
But one little hedgehog is singing along,
"Tra-la-la! I love Daddy!" he cries.

All the little ones
snuggle in bed now.
They will doze off to
sleepy-land soon.
Through the windows their
night-lights are glowing,
Soft and shimmery,
just like the moon.

Goodnight, little badgers
and squirrels,
Sleep tight, little bears
and mice too,
Sweet dreams, little hedgehogs
and rabbits,
And night-night and sweet
dreams to YOU!

More wonderful stories to read with your little one!

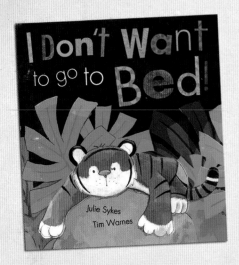

I Don't Want to go to Bed!
Julie Sykes
Tim Warnes

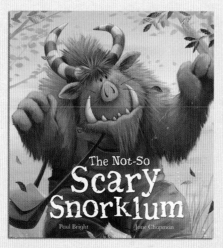

The Not-So Scary Snorklum
Paul Bright
Jane Chapman

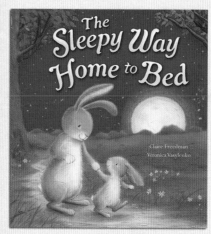

The Sleepy Way Home to Bed
Claire Freedman
Veronica Vasylenko

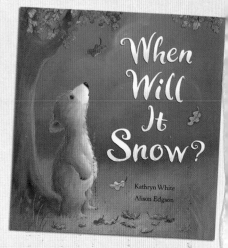

When Will It Snow?
Kathryn White
Alison Edgson

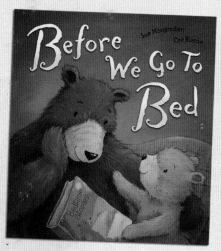

Before We Go To Bed
Sue Mongredien
Cee Biscoe

The Little White Owl
Tracey Corderoy
Jane Chapman

For information regarding any of the above titles
or for our catalogue, please contact us:
Little Tiger Press, 1 The Coda Centre,
189 Munster Road, London SW6 6AW
Tel: 020 7385 6333 • Fax: 020 7385 7333
E-mail: info@littletiger.co.uk
www.littletigerpress.com